bright spark

brilliant brain

cool kid

superstar

great work

GW00357514

Spelling

Written by Brenda Apsley

Illustrated by John Haslam

 This book belongs to

....

EGMONT

Tips for happy home learning

Make learning fun by working at your child's pace
and always giving tasks which s/he can do.
Tasks that are too difficult will discourage
her/him from trying again.

Give encouragement and praise and remember
to award gold stars and sticker badges for
effort as well as good work.

Always do too little rather than too much,
and finish each session on a positive note.

Don't work when you or your child
is tired or hungry.

Reinforce workbook activities and new ideas by
making use of real objects around the home.

EGMONT
We bring stories to life

Printed in Italy.
ISBN 1 4052 1565 8
4 6 8 10 9 7 5

Write the first letters to spell the words.
The pictures will help you.
There is one word for each letter of the alphabet.
Cross out the alphabet letters as you write them.

a̸ b c d e f g h i j k l

a n t

_ e e

_ a t

_ o g

_ g g

_ i s h

_ a t e

_ a t

_ n k

_ u g

_ i t e

_ o g

m n o p q r s t u v w x y z

_ o p

_ e t

_ r a n g e

_ a n

_ u e e n

_ u g

_ u n

_ o y

_ p

_ a n

_ e b

_ - r a y

_ o - yo

_ i p

Now you know all your letters!

Write **a** to spell the words. Spell each word twice.

vn
_ _ _

c _ p
_ _ _

j _ m
_ _ _

b _ g
_ _ _

m _ n
_ _ _

h _ t
_ _ _

c _ t
_ _ _

f _ n
_ _ _

The cat sat on the _m_a_t_ .   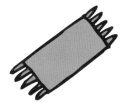   fat   hat   mat

The man has a _ _ _ .      pan   hat   map

The _ _ _ is black.      sat   hat   bat

Here are six _ _ _ _ _ .      cats   hats   mats

Note for parents: The vowel **a** has a short, hard sound in these words.

6 Words with **e**

Write **e** to spell the words. Spell each word twice.

b _ d   b _ l l   p _ g   t _ n

_ _ _   _ _ _ _   _ _ _   _ _ _

n _ t   h _ n   n _ s t   t _ d d y

_ _ _   _ _ _   _ _ _ _   _ _ _ _ _

Choose the right words. Spell them.

The table has four _ _ _ _ _ .      legs   pegs   beds

Here are three _ _ _ _ _ .      hens   eggs   pens

The teddy is on the _ _ _ .      net   red   bed

Here are _ _ _ pegs.      ten   beds   pegs

 Super spelling, choose a sticker!

Write **i** to spell the words. Spell each word twice.

l _ d   p _ n   z _ p   b _ n

_ _ _   _ _ _   _ _ _   _ _ _

w _ g   b _ b   h _ l l   k _ n g

_ _ _   _ _ _   _ _ _ _   _ _ _ _

Write **o** to spell the words. Spell each word twice.

c _ t   d _ g   m _ p   p _ t

_ _ _   _ _ _   _ _ _   _ _ _

h _ p   d _ l l   b _ x   t _ p

_ _ _   _ _ _ _   _ _ _   _ _ _

Words with **i**, **o** and **u**

Write **u** to spell the words. Spell each word twice.

c _ p

_ _ _

t _ b

_ _ _

b _ n

_ _ _

s _ n

_ _ _

m _ m

_ _ _

s _ m

_ _ _

h _ t

_ _ _

r _ g

_ _ _

Choose the right words. Spell them.

The _ _ _ is in the sky.      bun   top   sun

The bag has a _ _ _ .      zip   cup   pup

Here is a _ _ _ .      tip   cup   lip

The dog is _ _ _ .      pip   bib   big

Note for parents: Simple, single syllable words are the first words your child will be able to read and spell.

Do the letter sums to spell the **ck** words.
Draw lines to match the words to the pictures.

du + ck = _ _ _ _

so + ck = _ _ _ _

ki + ck = _ _ _ _

sa + ck = _ _ _ _

ne + ck = _ _ _ _

The letters **st** can start and end words.
Write the words that finish the sentences.
Choose from the list.

last   start   first   stop   fast   step   lost

Dan ran fast right from the _ _ _ _ _ _ .

He came _ _ _ _ _ in the race.

Ben ran slowly. He came _ _ _ _ .

Well done, you are working well.

Write **ch** or **sh** to spell the words. Spell each word twice.

f i _ _

_ _ _ _

_ _ i m p

_ _ _ _ _

_ _ e l l

_ _ _ _ _

_ _ a i r

_ _ _ _ _

_ _ i p

_ _ _ _

_ _ u r _ _

_ _ _ _ _ _

Choose the right **th** words. Spell them.

My parents are my _ _ _ _ _ _ _ and _ _ _ _ _ _ _ .

mother   brother   father

I like having a _ _ _ _ .

think   bath   path

The shark has sharp _ _ _ _ _ _ .

teeth   them   thread

The _ _ _ _ was very steep.

there   the   path

Words with 'magic e'

When the letter **e** is added to the end of a word it changes the word. So **man** becomes **mane**.

Add '**magic e**' to make new words.

cap + e = _ _ _ _

tap + e = _ _ _ _

can + e = _ _ _ _

pan + e = _ _ _ _

Draw lines to match the old word with the new word.

pin _   tube

tub _   cube

cub _   pine

Words with 'magic e'

Find these '**magic e**' words in the wordsquare.
Look left to right, right to left, up and down.
The first word is done to show you how.

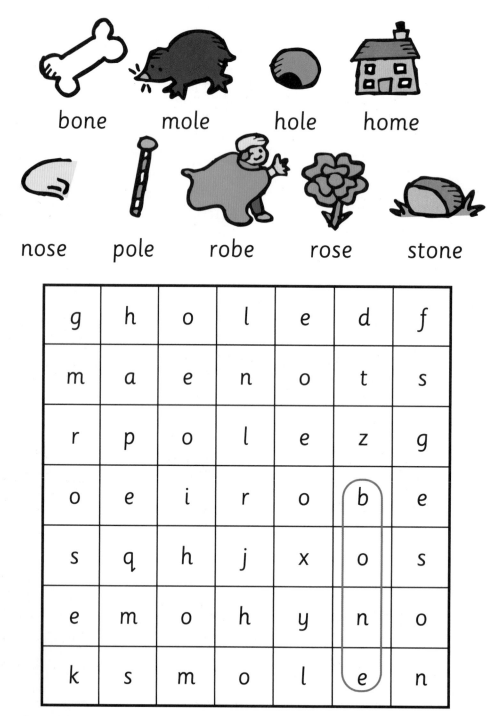

bone   mole   hole   home

nose   pole   robe   rose   stone

g	h	o	l	e	d	f
m	a	e	n	o	t	s
r	p	o	l	e	z	g
o	e	i	r	o	b	e
s	q	h	j	x	o	s
e	m	o	h	y	n	o
k	s	m	o	l	e	n

Note for parents: Older children could think of more examples
of 'magic e' words and list them in a spelling book.

Match the letters to spell words. Spell each word twice.

b l

_ _ a c k

_ _ _ _ _

_ _ o c k

_ _ _ _ _

_ _ i n k

_ _ _ _ _

c l

_ _ a p

_ _ _ _

_ _ a y

_ _ _ _

_ _ i p

_ _ _ _

f l

_ _ a g

_ _ _ _

_ _ y

_ _ _

_ _ a t

_ _ _ _

g l

_ _ a s s

_ _ _ _ _

_ _ u e

_ _ _ _

_ _ o v e

_ _ _ _ _

p l

_ _ a y

_ _ _ _

_ _ u m

_ _ _ _

_ _ a n t

_ _ _ _ _

s l

_ _ o w

_ _ _ _

_ _ i p

_ _ _ _

_ _ e e p

_ _ _ _ _

Splendid spelling!

Words with **br**, **cr**, **dr**, **fr**, **gr**, **tr**

Match the letters to spell words. Spell each word twice.

br >

_ _ i c k

_ _ i d g e

_ _ i m

_ _ _ _ _   _ _ _ _ _   _ _ _ _ _

cr >

_ _ a b

_ _ y

_ _ e a m

_ _ _ _ _   _ _ _ _ _   _ _ _ _ _

dr >

_ _ i p

_ _ e s s

_ _ a w

_ _ _ _ _   _ _ _ _ _   _ _ _ _ _

fr >

_ _ o g

_ _ y

_ _ o s t

_ _ _ _ _   _ _ _   _ _ _ _ _

gr >

_ _ o w

_ _ a p e

_ _ a s s

_ _ _ _ _   _ _ _ _ _   _ _ _ _ _

tr >

_ _ e e

_ _ a i n

_ _ i c k

_ _ _ _ _   _ _ _ _ _   _ _ _ _ _

Note for parents: Ask your child to think of some more words that begin with these sounds.

Write **oo** to spell the words.
Draw lines to match the words to the pictures.

s p _ _ n

m _ _ n

b _ _ t

b a l l _ _ n

s c h _ _ l

Write **ee** to finish the spelling sums.
Draw lines to match the words and pictures.

b + e e = _ _ _

f + e e + t = _ _ _ _

t r + e e = _ _ _ _

p + e e + p = _ _ _ _

s l + e e + p = _ _ _ _ _

Spell the double letter words.
Choose the letters from the list.

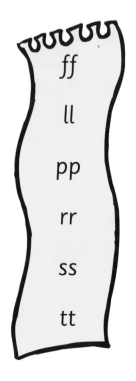

ff

ll

pp

rr

ss

tt

t o _ _ e e   f i _ _   p e _ _ e r

n a _ _ y   b a _ _   b e _ _

p a _ _ o t   p u _ _ y   k i _ _ e n

g r a _ _   g l a _ _   h i _ _

l o _ _ y   c a _ _ o t   w a _ _

Read the rhyme. Underline the double letter words.
Look for **ee**, **ll**, **mm** and **tt**.

Three little kittens they lost their mittens,

And they began to cry.

"Oh, Mummy dear, we greatly fear,

Our mittens we have lost."

"What? Lost your mittens?

You naughty kittens! Now you shall have no pie!"

 Well done! You are good at this.

The letter **u** always comes after the letter **q**.
The letters **qu** sound like **kw** as in queen.
Read this story. Underline all the **qu** words you can find.

"Quick!" said the queen. "It's a quarter-past seven.

Turn on the TV. There's a new quiz show I want to

watch. Quickly now!"

The king turned on the TV, but he didn't watch the quiz

show. He lay on the sofa under a warm quilt. It was quite

warm, and soon the king was fast asleep. He started to snore.

"Be quiet!" the queen cried. "I can't hear the questions!"

"Shan't!" said the king.

Oh dear, do you think they were going to have a quarrel?

Are you working quickly and quietly?

The letters **kn** make the sound of n. The **k** is always 'silent'. You write it but you do not say it.
Write **kn** to spell the words.
Draw lines to match the words to the pictures.

_ _ e e

_ _ i f e

_ _ o t

_ _ i t

_ _ o b

The letters **wh** sound like w. The letter **w** is 'silent'.
Write **wh** to spell the words.
Lots of **wh** words ask questions.
Draw circles around the words that ask questions.

_ _ e e l   (_ _ y)   _ _ a t   _ _ i t e

_ _ e n   _ _ e r e   _ _ i c h   _ _ i s p e r

Brilliant! You are good with silent letters.

The letters **oa** and **ow** both sound like o in these words.
Choose the right words from the lists. Spell them.

foal
goat
moat
loaf
soap
boat

A _ _ _ _ of bread.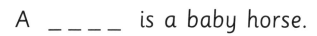

A _ _ _ _ is a baby horse.

A _ _ _ _ goes on water.

I wash with _ _ _ _ .

slow
grows
mows
crow
blow
snows

A _ _ _ _ snail.

A black _ _ _ _ .

I _ _ _ _ out my candles.

It _ _ _ _ _ in winter.

Goodness me! You are very clever.

20 Words with **ou** and **ow**

The letters **ou** and **ow** sound the same in these words.
Choose the right words from the lists. Spell them.

loud
house
pound
out
shout
mound

In and _ _ _ .

100 pence make 1 _ _ _ _ _ _ .

I live in a _ _ _ _ _ _ .

The music is _ _ _ _ _ .

cow
down
owl
frown
towel
clown

An _ _ _ is a bird with big eyes.

A _ _ _ gives us milk.

Up and _ _ _ _ .

I dry myself with a _ _ _ _ _ _ .

Notes for parents: There is no spelling rule to follow here.
Children should learn these words by heart.

Write **ai** to spell these words. Spell each word twice.

t _ _ l   r _ _ n   n _ _ l   g r _ _ n

_ _ _ _   _ _ _ _   _ _ _ _   _ _ _ _ _

t r _ _ n   s n _ _ l   h _ _ r   c h _ _ r

_ _ _ _ _   _ _ _ _ _   _ _ _ _   _ _ _ _ _

Choose the right words. Spell them.

Brush your _ _ _ _ .

hair   fair   chair

Jack and Jill went to fetch a _ _ _ _ of water.

rail   pail   bail

We went to the _ _ _ _ .

fair   mail   gain

The postman delivers _ _ _ _ .

snail   mail   grain

Excellent work again!

Some words with **ea** have a l-o-n-g sound, as in **east**. Some words with **ea** have a short sound, as in **head**. Look at the words and pictures. Which ea sound do they have? Spell the words on the lines.

teacher   seat   teapot   feather

treasure   bread   beads   head

l-o-n-g **ea** as in east   short **ea** as in head

_____   _____

_____   _____

_____   _____

_____   _____

Write **ay** to spell the words. Spell each word twice.

h _ _   b _ _   t r _ _   p l _ _

_ _ _   _ _ _   _ _ _ _   _ _ _ _

c l _ _   r _ _   p _ _   p r _ _

_ _ _ _   _ _ _   _ _ _   _ _ _ _

Choose the right words. Spell them.

Boys and girls go out to _ _ _ _ .

pay   play   say

We make models with _ _ _ _ .

clay   hay   bay

Can you _ _ _ the letters of the alphabet?

say   may   lay

The hen _ _ _ _ eggs.

says   lays   prays

How many eggs has the hen laid?

The letters **ight** make a sound like **ite**. The **g** and **h** are 'silent' letters. Write **ight** to spell the words. Spell each word twice.

n _ _ _ _   r _ _ _ _   f _ _ _ _

_ _ _ _ _   _ _ _ _ _   _ _ _ _ _

l _ _ _ _   k n _ _ _ _   f r _ _ _ _

_ _ _ _ _   _ _ _ _ _ _   _ _ _ _ _ _

Choose the right words. Spell them.

The stars are _ _ _ _ _ _ _ .

bright   might

Left and _ _ _ _ _ _ .

fight   right

The plane set off on its _ _ _ _ _ _ _ .

flight   fight

How tall you are is your _ _ _ _ _ _ _ .

sight   height

Adding **ing**

Lots of verbs or doing words end in **ing**.
For example, **walking** and **jumping** are verbs.
When you add **ing** to a verb that ends in **e**, the **e**
disappears. For example: **I make** but **I am making**.

m a k e + i n g = m a k i n g

Spell these words by adding **ing**.

We are _ _ _ _ _ _ _ .   We are _ _ _ _ _ _ _ .

She is _ _ _ _ _ _ .   She is _ _ _ _ _ _ .

They are _ _ _ _ _ _ .   They are _ _ _ _ _ _ .

I am _ _ _ _ _ _ _ .   I am _ _ _ _ _ _ _ .

He is _ _ _ _ _ _ _ .   He is _ _ _ _ _ _ _ .

Choose the right **ing** words from the list. Spell them.

hoping   sliding   biting   using   writing   taking

I am _ _ _ _ _ a pencil and ruler to draw a line.

I am _ _ _ _ _ _ to get a computer for my birthday.

In winter I like _ _ _ _ _ _ _ on the ice.

Note for parents: Make a spelling list of other verbs that
your child is able to do her/himself and keep adding to it.

Adding ing

Look what happens to these words when we add **ing**.

hop + ing = hopping

shop + ing = shopping

run + ing = running

clap + ing = clapping

swim + ing = swimming

Choose the right **ing** words from the list. Spell them.

sipping   cutting   getting   winning   letting   hitting

I am _ _ _ _ _ _ _ ready for bed.

I am _ _ _ _ _ _ _ my drink.

I am _ _ _ _ _ _ _ some paper.

Note to parents: With older children, point to the vowel before the last letter to explain the spelling rule.

A plural word is one that means more than one of something, as in **boys**.

Some words are made into plural words by adding **s** at the end. Spell the plural words by adding **s**.

one ball   two _ _ _ _ _ _

one bun   two _ _ _ _

one mug   two _ _ _ _

Some words are made into plural words by adding **es** at the end. This happens when the words end in **ch**, **sh**, **s**, **ss** or **x**. Spell the plural words by adding **es**.

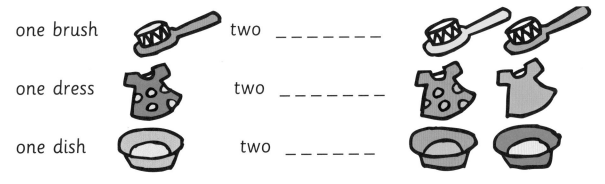

one brush   two _ _ _ _ _ _ _ _

one dress   two _ _ _ _ _ _ _

one dish   two _ _ _ _ _ _

Spell the plural word for each set of things.

_ _ _ _   _ _ _ _ _ _ _

Adding s

To spell plurals of some words that end in the letter **y**, add **s**. For example, one **day** and two **days**. For some words that end in **y** write **ies** instead of **y**: one **party**, two **parties**.

Spell the plural words by writing **ies** instead of **y**.

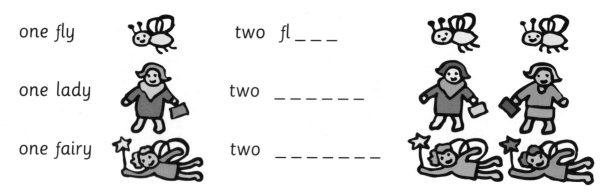

one fly   two fl _ _ _

one lady   two _ _ _ _ _ _

one fairy   two _ _ _ _ _ _

The plural words for some things are quite different. Read the words. Draw lines to match them.

goose   mouse   child   man   die   foot

men   geese   dice   children   feet   mice

But, some words stay the same:

one sheep   two sheep

Wonderful work! Choose a sticker.

Words that rhyme are words that sound the same. They often have the same letter endings, like **big** and **dig**, **cat** and **hat**.

Draw lines to join two words that rhyme with the picture clue words.

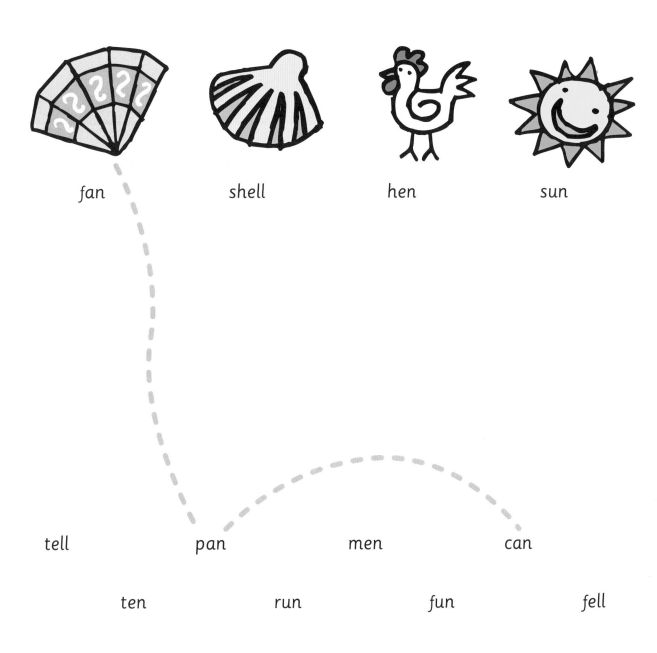

fan   shell   hen   sun

tell   pan   men   can

ten   run   fun   fell

That was easy peasy!

Spell the numbers one to ten.
Spell each number word twice.

one   _ _ _   _ _ _

two   _ _ _   _ _ _

thr _ _   _ _ _ _ _   _ _ _ _ _

f _ _ r   _ _ _ _   _ _ _ _

f _ v _   _ _ _ _   _ _ _ _

six   _ _ _   _ _ _

s _ v _ n   _ _ _ _ _   _ _ _ _ _

ei _ _ _   _ _ _ _ _   _ _ _ _ _

n _ n _   _ _ _ _   _ _ _ _

t _ n   _ _ _   _ _ _

Now spell the numbers eleven to twenty.
Spell each number word twice.

el _ v _ n   _ _ _ _ _ _   _ _ _ _ _ _

tw _ lve   _ _ _ _ _ _   _ _ _ _ _ _

thirt _ _ n   _ _ _ _ _ _ _ _ _ _ _ _ _ _ _ _

fourt _ _ n   _ _ _ _ _ _ _ _ _ _ _ _ _ _ _ _

fif _ _ _ _   _ _ _ _ _ _ _   _ _ _ _ _ _ _

six _ _ _ _   _ _ _ _ _ _ _   _ _ _ _ _ _ _

seven _ _ _ _   _ _ _ _ _ _ _ _ _ _ _ _ _ _ _ _ _ _

eight _ _ n   _ _ _ _ _ _ _ _ _ _ _ _ _ _ _ _

n _ n _ teen   _ _ _ _ _ _ _ _ _ _ _ _ _ _ _ _

tw _ nty   _ _ _ _ _ _   _ _ _ _ _ _

Which word says how old you are?

Day is an **ay** word. So is **today**.
Add **day** on to each word spell the days of the week.
Spell each word twice.

Sun _ _ _   _ _ _ _ _ _

Mon _ _ _   _ _ _ _ _ _

Tues _ _ _   _ _ _ _ _ _ _

Wednes _ _ _   _ _ _ _ _ _ _ _ _

Thurs _ _ _   _ _ _ _ _ _ _ _

Fri _ _ _   _ _ _ _ _ _

Satur _ _ _   _ _ _ _ _ _ _ _

What day is it today? Today is _____.

My favourite day is _____.

Learn to spell the months of the year, using a calendar to help you. Spell each month twice.

Jan _ _ _ _

_ _ _ _ _ _ _ _

Febr _ _ _ _ _

_ _ _ _ _ _ _ _

Mar _ _

_ _ _ _ _

Apr _ _

_ _ _ _ _

M _ _

_ _ _

J _ n _

_ _ _ _

Jul _

_ _ _ _

Augu _ _

_ _ _ _ _ _

Sept _ _ _ _ _ _

_ _ _ _ _ _ _ _ _

Octo _ _ _

_ _ _ _ _ _ _

Nov _ _ _ _ _

_ _ _ _ _ _ _ _

Dec _ _ _ _ _ _

_ _ _ _ _ _ _ _

Spell the month we are in now. _____

Spell the month of your birthday. _____

Super smart! Have a star!